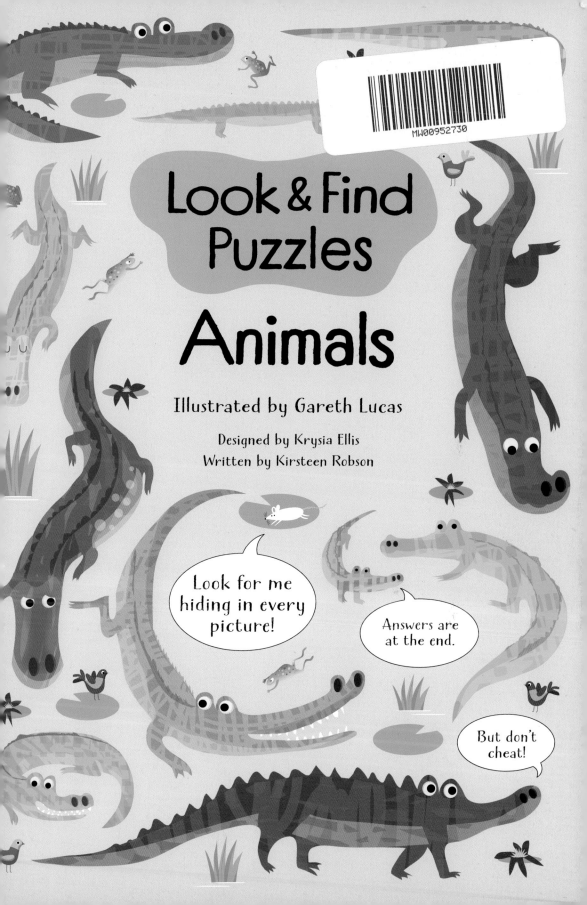

Find four lion cubs with their mother.

Can you find...

another 2 golden crowns

3 more brown mice

2

2 other
bananas

3 more birds,
just like this

another
sleeping lion

I've lost my kite! Have you seen it?

Look for a bird with a bell.

Can you find...   2 different toucans   another 3 green bugs

Can you spot a pirate parrot?

5 more pink flowers like this

another bird balloon

1 other egg

Who's holding his sister's tail?

Spot a crocodile.

Can you find...   3 more running flamingos   another 2 fishing nets

1 other elephant
squirting water

3 more pink
butterflies

another hippo
in a hurry

Look for a hissing snake.

Can you find...

another 5 birds like this

3 more bees

8

2 other
bags

1 more
giraffe mug

another
striped cat

Spot a frog wearing flippers.

Can you find...		10 other flies		another white lily flower

Spot a sleeping owl.

Where is my twin brother?

Can you find...

1 more bat like this

another 2 squirrels

14

Can you find... 3 other different caterpillars 1 more moth like this

another snake
with its eyes shut

3 more straw
hats

1 other scarf
like this

Where's my rubber ring?

Can you find...

6 more frogs

another 3 birds like this

18

2 other different toothbrushes

2 more tubes of toothpaste

another tooth-cleaning bird

Spot a bee.

Can you spy two spiders?

Can you find...

2 other flowery bugs

3 more like this

Who else has a shell like mine?

Spot two turtle tots on Grandpa's back.

Can you find...

another 5 starfish

4 more blue beach balls

Find a broken bead bracelet.

3 other shells like this

another 2 red buckets

2 more of these

Can you find my cub, who's just like me?

Whose tail has no stripes?

Can you find...

5 other hats, all different

1 more bird like this

another 3
apples

5 more twigs
with 5 leaves

1 other white-
striped tail

Who is wearing the longest scarf?

Have you seen a snow person?

Can you find...

2 more just like this

another 5 green balls

Which penguin doesn't have a hat or a scarf?

1 other penguin with an egg

2 more carrots

another hat like this

Answers

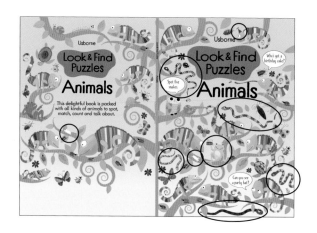

Cover

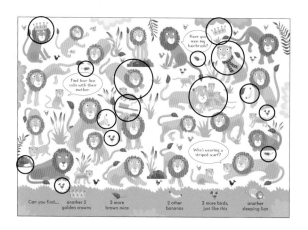

2-3

4-5

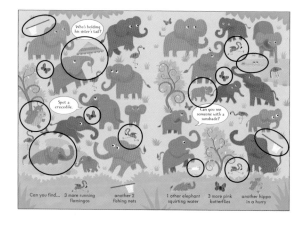

6-7

8-9

30

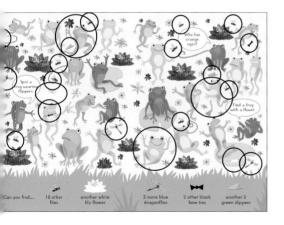

10–11

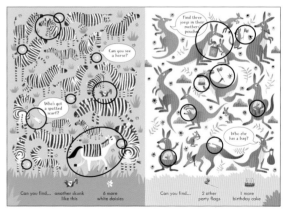

12–13

14–15

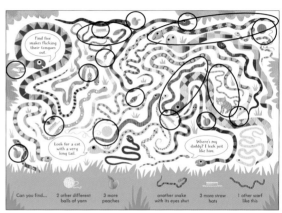

16–17

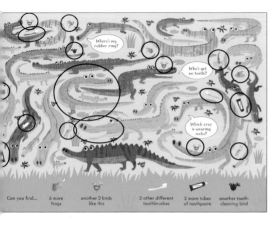

18–19

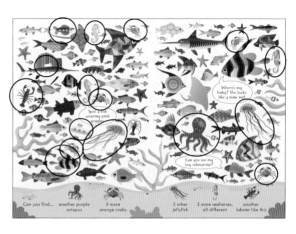

20–21

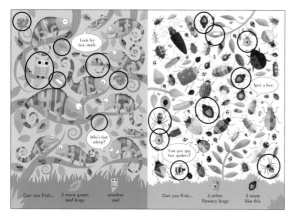

22–23

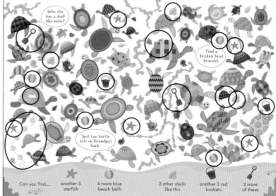

24–25

26–27

28–29

First published in 2022 by Usborne Publishing Ltd, Usborne House, 83-85 Saffron Hill, London, EC1N 8RT, England.
usborne.com © 2022 Usborne Publishing Ltd. The name Usborne and the Balloon logo are trade marks of Usborne
Publishing Ltd. All rights reserved. No part of this publication may be reproduced, stored in a retrieval system, or
transmitted in any form or by any means without the prior permission of the publisher. UE. Printed in China.